FUN ON WHEELS

BY CORINN CODYE

Reading Skills for Life

Level A

Book 1

AGS®

American Guidance Service , Inc.
Circle Pines, Minnesota 55014-1796
1-800-328-2560

Development and editorial services provided by Straight Line Editorial
Development, Inc.

Illustrations: Wendy Cantor

Printed in the United States of America

ISBN 0-7854-2649-3

Product Number 91703

A 0 9 8 7 6 5 4

Contents

1. Bike Shop Job

Jed came racing up to the shop on his beat-up red BMX bike at top speed. He skidded to a stop. He jumped off the seat and bent down to lock his bike to the rack. Then he slipped off his helmet and held it by the strap. It hung from his left hand as he went into the shop.

In the shop, Jed looked up at the clock. He was thinking, I am on time for my job interview. He fished his job application from his back pocket.

"Is that you, Jed?" said a man who was at the back part of the shop. "Hang on. I will be out there in a bit. In fact, come on back. I have just one wheel left to fix. Say, what do you think of those new racing bikes?"

"I think they are red hot!" said Jed. "Are they as fast as they look?" He went to the back of the shop and sat down. Bill was spinning the back wheel of an upside-down bike. "But I am thinking about cars now, not bikes," Jed said. "I need a car."

Bill White had run the Wheels and Deals Bike Shop for many years. Jed got his first bike there, from Bill. Jed had been only 8 years old then. Now he was 17.

Many of the kids at school had cars. Jed was at the end of 11th grade and still no car! It was a joke at school. All the other kids were riding in their cars, and there he was on his beat-up red bike. He just had to get a car by the next school year! And getting a job was the way Jed was going to do it.

Up to now, Jed had just had kid-sitting jobs. He liked being with the kids, and they liked him. But the rate was only two bucks for each kid. It did not add up fast. That was OK for getting some pocket cash, but it would not cut it for getting a car. At times, Bill White at the bike shop gave jobs to kids who were in school. The first step in Jed's dream was to get one of those jobs and save some cash. With the savings, he could get a car for school next year.

"So you want a job so you can get a car and give up bikes!" joked Bill. "Did you bring back the job application?"

"I have it all filled out," said Jed. He opened up the application, pressed it flat, and handed it to Bill. "Yep, I think it is time to get a car. And just so you know, I still like riding bikes," he added.

"Jed," said Bill, looking over the application

quickly, "I know you well. I know your mom. You are a good kid. You know how to fix bikes. After all, you have been coming in here and fixing your own bike for years. I do not have to read all this. I would like to give you this job. Can you come in three times a week after school?"

Jed broke into a smile. "You mean, that is all? You are going to give me the job?"

"Yes, if you want it," said Bill. "If I did not know you, I would have to read each line of the application. I would have to call up the people you know and ask them about you. But I know you. I think you can do the work. Do you want the job?"

"Yes, Bill, yes!" said Jed. "When do I start?"

Jed and Bill worked out a plan for Jed to come in three times a week. He would work from 4:00 P.M. to 8:00 P.M. His first day would be May 1, in just two days.

Jed raced home on his bike. He rushed in and sat down at his desk. How much would he be bringing home each week? He got out a pad and pen and did some math. His rate would be $7.00. Yes! He was to work three days a week, from 4:00 to 8:00 P.M. So that would be three days, times four hours, times $7.00.

He put some numbers on the pad:

$$3 \text{ days} \times 4 = 12$$

$$12 \times \$7.00 = \$84.00 \text{ a week}$$

$$\text{Each day} = 4 \times \$7.00 = \$28.00 \text{ a day}$$

He looked at the numbers on the pad. That felt good. He could bring home $28.00 each day, or $84.00 a week!

On May 1, Jed rode to work after school feeling good. He did well at the job. He did know how to fix bikes. And he liked speaking with the people who came into the shop.

On the days when he was not working, Jed went looking at cars. New cars had top prices, way, way out of his reach. So he went by some used car lots. He saw with some shock that those prices for cars were steep as well. He looked in the ads and talked to people at school. It seemed like he would need to save more than $2,000 to get a car. It could be that he would need $3,000. Nope, he did not want a car so cheap or so run down that it would need fixing all the time.

At home, he spoke to his mom. He asked her if she could help him get a car. She looked at him as if she would like to help. But he had a feel for what she was going to say, before she said a thing.

"Jed, I would like very much to help you. But you know that I have to work two jobs now. I am just making ends meet for us as it is." His mom looked at him over her glasses. "This plan, this car, will have to be your thing, all the way. I know you can do it, if you work at it."

Then she said, "But remember, there are other costs as well. You must shell out cash for gas and taxes, and for fixing the car." She helped him make a list of all the costs.

Car Costs for One Year

get a car	$1,000
insurance	600
gas	500
fix-ups	450
Total	**$2,550**

Jed sat down with his pad and pen. He was thinking, How much can I save up before the next school year, working at the shop? He ticked through the coming weeks. School would get going in about 16 weeks. He would get $84.00 each week, times 16 weeks.

$$\$84.00 \times 16 = \$1,344.00$$

Only $1,344.00! Yikes! This was not good. He would need over $1,000 more to get the car.

The next day, Jed got his first check from Bill White. Bill had left it for him on the desk at the back of the shop. It felt so good to have the check in his hands! Jed looked at the check: $152.00. What? That did not sound right! Jed did some fast math:

$84.00 each week x 2 weeks = $168.00

What was this? Why was the check not made out for $168.00? Did Bill know what he was doing? Jed did not think that Bill would cheat him. He looked close up at the check stub. Some numbers were there. Rate $7.00 × 24 = $168.00, less taxes of $16.00. Taxes? What are those?

Jed did not need a pad and pen to do the math. He could see right then that his dream of getting a car was way out of reach! He was not getting $84.00 each week. He was getting just $76.00. He locked up the shop and got on his bike. All the pep seemed to leak out of him. His feet did not want to push the bike at all. It was just like a bad, bad dream—a dream where he was 25 or 30 and still on a bike.

2. A Plan Takes Shape

It was a shock to find out that taxes must come out of his checks, but Jed got over it. In fact, he liked working at the bike shop a lot. He liked fixing bikes for people and helping them look at things in the shop. He liked it when they asked him things. He liked joking with the kids who came into the shop and speaking with their moms and dads.

And there was one other thing he liked about the job—Amanda. Amanda was 18 years old, just out of 12th grade. Most of the time, Amanda worked at the shop on days when Jed was not there. Some days, Jed and Amanda worked at the same time. Jed liked that. Amanda was fun to chat with. Now and then they went out for a snack after work.

But Amanda was only going to be at the shop for two more weeks. After school let out, she would be going to work at a camp for kids.

Jed was not at all happy that Amanda was going. And he was finding out that he could not save all the funds that he made on the job. He had to have a little cash just for spending. He needed it for getting snacks, eating at school, keeping his bike fixed, and doing things for fun from time to time. Now that he was working, he felt bad asking his mom for cash.

One day Amanda was telling Jed and Bill about the camp she was going to. Two moms and their kids were in the shop right then. The moms jumped right in, asking about camps for their kids.

"We are looking for some fun things for our kids to do when school gets out," one mom said. "They need a place to go each day to run, jump, swim, hike, or ride."

"Yes," said the other mom. "We do not want them to just sit at home and look at TV all day."

"The camp where I am going is not close by," said Amanda. "And the kids go for two weeks at a time, not just for the day."

"We will let you know if we find out about a day camp," said Bill to the two moms. "Good luck looking."

After that, Jed got to thinking. Many moms and dads who came into the shop were looking for fun things for the kids to do when school was out. It seemed like the city needed some day camps, or some places for kids to go. The next day, Jed and Bill were dusting the new bikes and cleaning the shop. "How are the savings for a car going, Jed?" Bill asked.

Jed looked a little sad. He said, "I am saving most of what I make from this job, but it is not adding up very fast. I think I will need a lot more for a car. I mean, at first, I did not even know that you had to take out taxes from my check. I do not know how long it will be before I can get a car."

"I hope it helps to know that I think you are doing a good job here," Bill said. "How would you like to have more time at work? Amanda is leaving after next week. Would you like to have her days? That would give you at least two more days a week. It might help you a little with the car plans."

"You bet I would like that," said Jed. "Thanks, Bill. Each little bit is a help!" Jed stopped dusting for a bit. "You know, Bill, I am thinking a lot about this day camp thing. So many moms are looking for stuff their kids can do out in the sun."

"What do you mean?" Bill asked.

"Well, I have looked after kids before. I like playing with them. All the kids who come in here have bikes. I have a bike. I like bike riding. Do you think those moms would like some one—like me—to take their kids out bike riding each day?"

Bill stopped what he was doing and looked at Jed. "Say, Jed, I think that could be a good deal for the moms," he said. "Hmmm. Let me think about that some. The bike shop could do that, open up a biking day camp. I tell you what. When you go home, try to come up with a plan. Make a list of what we would need to do to set up this biking day camp. I will think about it as well."

Over the next three days, Bill and Jed spoke more about the day camp. It was looking like a great plan! Bill seemed to think they could get kids for the camp from the moms and dads who came into the shop. Plus, it would bring more people into the shop. And the kids would be getting more into riding, so the shop would sell more bike stuff.

They spoke about having lots of fun things for the kids to do. Jed could take them riding to neat places in the city. They could go swimming, fishing, and hiking. They could go places to play team games as well.

Bill and Jed came up with a plan for how the day camp could work. Moms and dads could drop off their kids by 10:00 A.M. The kids would bring a bag with sun block and things to eat and drink for the day. Jed would take them out on their bikes. They would be out till 3:00 P.M. Then they would come back to the bike shop. After that, the moms and dads could pick up their kids.

Then, after 4:00 P.M., Jed could keep working in the shop till closing time. He would not have to give up his work at the shop.

Jed felt good about all this. He felt good that Bill liked the plan. But would moms and dads want this kind of day camp? Would they feel their kids would be safe with him, out on their bikes all day? How many kids could he look after at one time? What would it cost for each kid? Jed had a lot more to think about.

3. The Chase

One day Jed was in the back of the shop. He was bent over the rim of a bike wheel, trying to fix it. Bill was out of the shop.

A sound came from the shop. What was that? Jed stopped working on the wheel. He stepped into the shop just in time! A kid was wheeling one of the new bikes right out of the shop!

"Stop!" Jed yelled. The kid looked at him and kept on going. He was in the street with the bike. "Stop, you!" Jed yelled one more time. Then he went after the kid.

The kid was up on the bike. He was speeding down the street. Jed lit out like a rocket. His legs pumped fast. The kid on the bike picked up speed. "I am not going to get him," Jed was thinking. "That bike is fast!" He was getting winded from running. Then he got mad. What made that kid think he could take a bike that was not his? "I am going to get you now!" he yelled.

The kid looked back at the sound of Jed yelling. Not a good thing to do. One wheel of the snappy new bike hit a rock. The bike slid out from under the kid. He let out a yell of pain as he fell. He pushed the bike off him. He looked this way and that for a place to run. But then Jed was all over him.

"What do you think you are doing?" Jed yelled as he yanked the kid up. Just then Bill came up the street. He was huffing and puffing.

"I called the cops," Bill said. "They are on the way." He looked at Jed. "Are you OK?" he asked. "I spotted you going after that kid just as I was getting back. I could tell he was trying to make off with one of our bikes. That was fast thinking, Jed—and fast running!"

Jed was winded, but he was OK. "I will take over now," Bill said. "You take this bike back to the shop." Jed let go of the kid and picked up the bike. It looked OK.

A cop got there fast. She led the kid to her car. Then it was all over.

"You did a fine job," Bill said to Jed. "I see that you can think fast. But next time, just call the cops. Do not go running after the creep. We need to keep you safe and sound. You have to run our day camp, after all!"

"I was thinking about a name for the camp," Jed said. "What about Fun on Wheels?"

"Fun on Wheels Day Camp. That has a nice ring to it," said Bill.

Bill and Jed went over their plans some more. Bill had come up with a plan for how the cash part would work. "I think we can ask about $15.00 a day from moms and dads."

"And Jed, I would like you to have $10.00 for each kid, each day," said Bill. "The shop will keep $5.00."

Jed felt good. This was more than he had hoped for.

"That seems OK," Jed said. "How many kids do you think I can ride with at one time?"

"I think you could work with about six kids," said Bill. "We will ask the moms and dads to bring the kids into the day camp for one week at a time.

"The other thing is, I think we need to say that the camp is for 8- to 10-year-old kids only. If they are not that old, it may not be easy to keep them all going at the same pace. What do you think?"

Jed nodded yes. "I want to keep them on the go." He was thinking about the fun of riding bikes all over the city. He did not think it would be so fun to have little kids keeping them back.

Bill went on. "The other thing is, moms and dads will have to feel safe about leaving their kids with you." Jed nodded but was not feeling so good any more.

"I want you to think more about how you will keep all the kids safe," said Bill. "I want you to plan now what you will do if things do not go right while you are out riding or playing."

Then Bill said, "But you need to do more than just think. I want you to take a CPR class. See if you can get into a class this weekend. It may cost you $25.00 or so."

Jed now felt a little sick. Things were getting out of hand. Think about this! Think about that! Take a class! Spend $25.00! For a bit Jed felt like giving up. But just then he heard a car zip past. He was thinking, For a ride like that, I will stick with it.

"You are right," said Jed. "These are good things to think about. And I will take the class."

"Good," Bill said. "I think we need to get this ad up in the shop and in the news, so people will know about the day camp. I hope we can get going the first week in June, in just two weeks. That is the first week of school being out. What do you say?"

"I say, do it!" said Jed.

In the next two days, Jed and Bill got an ad up in the shop. Jed got into the CPR class. Then, as people came into the shop, they saw the ad and asked about Fun on Wheels. At the end of the next week, they had three kids on the list.

That was not as many kids as they had hoped for. Jed could see that the cash would be a lot less than he had planned. Still, Jed was thinking, it is a way to get going! We will still have Fun on Wheels. If it is as good as I think it will be, the kids will tell others. Their moms will tell other moms. More kids will come in as time goes by.

Jed grabbed his bike and hit the street. He was thinking, What a week! Still, a lot of stuff came out OK. Now I have to get some sleep, or those kids will make me feel 99 years old!

4. Jed Sets the Pace

At last! It was the first day of Fun on Wheels day camp! Jed could not sit still. At 9:30 A.M. he was pacing up and down in the shop. It was time for the kids to get there. He was thinking, Where are they? Will they flake? One by one, the kids came into the shop with their bikes. Jed greeted the kids. He spoke to the moms and dads. He checked that each child had a helmet, sun glasses, a day pack, water, things to eat, and sun block. By 9:50 he had all three kids—Kenny, Nisha, and Gwen. He gave the moms and dads some take-home sheets telling all the things the kids would do and the places they would go all week. He helped the kids put on their sun block, packs, and helmets.

Then, right at 10:00, one more kid came in. That is, his mom dragged him in. She had one hand on the kid and the other hand on his bike. This kid looked really mad, like he did not want to be going on a bike ride at all. "This is Jimmy," said the mom. "Can he be in the biking day camp this week?"

"Yes," said Jed. But he was thinking, I do not know about this one. "We have space for one or two more kids. Did you bring a helmet and a day pack with water—and things for Jimmy to eat?"

Jimmy's mom said, "Yes, I will get all those things from my car."

"And we will need $5.00 to rent a fishing pole," said Jed. "We are going fishing at the lake."

"OK. Hang on. I will be right back and write you a check for the week."

Jimmy stomped out of the shop and plopped down by the bike rack. His look said it all: I do not want to do this.

Jed got out some poles with green flags at the top. Printed on the flags was "Fun on Wheels VIP." He fixed each flag on a big pole, and then fixed each pole to a bike. The flags would help Jed see the kids while biking.

And they were off! That is, they were riding—but they did not look like a pack. The kids were riding all over the place! Kenny set off riding so fast that the others could not keep up. Jimmy, on the other hand, had stopped his bike. He was getting off and turning his bike back to the shop.

Then things got really bad. Nisha rushed out into the path of traffic. Gwen got to riding with no hands.

"OK, OK! Stop! Stop!" Jed yelled. "Get back here!" He called all the bikes back to him. He could see that this pack of kids needed some safe bike-riding tips. And fast!

Jed went over to Jimmy and sat down next to him. "Jimmy, do you like to ride?"

"No. I like to jump," said Jimmy. He kicked a rock.

"I tell you what," said Jed. "I know places that have lots of jumps. I think we will be doing some jumps. But if you want to do jumps, you will need to keep up with us."

The other kids dragged their bikes in close to Jed and Jimmy.

"Look," said Jed. "This camp is called Fun on Wheels. If we are going to have fun here, we will have to have some rules." He said, "First, we do not go off and leave one kid in back. We have to keep close to each other. Kenny, you are fast, buddy. But you must look back and see that we are all close by. Jimmy—I am going to call you Jimmy Jump. You are part of this! You must keep up, not just jump up. Plus, we all have to think about cars and the rules of traffic. So here we go with the riding rules:

"Rule number 1. You must ride safely at all times. This means keeping in one line and keeping in a pack. If I cannot see you, then we are not all safe. So I must see you all the time.

"That brings me to rule number 2. Rule number 2: Do not pass Jed! You got that, Kenny?"

Kenny nodded yes.

"Rule number 3: Stay all the way over to the right side of the traffic. Do not ride out in the way of the cars."

Jed grabbed Jimmy to make this speech more of a game. "And what are you going to do if we have to pass a car that is stopped at the side with no one in it?" He lifted Jimmy on to the seat of his bike and pushed that bike up to Nisha's bike. "You will have to look out for things in the way." He pushed the bike in a path so it missed Nisha's bike. Then he lifted it. "Or you could jump right over it. No! That was a joke!" Jimmy was grinning just a little bit. "You got rule number 3?"

They all nodded.

"Rule number 4: Look out for people getting out of cars. And rule number 5: Keep your chin up and look out. We do not want any crashes.

"And you have to know this. Jimmy, Nisha, Gwen, and Kenny: You are all VIPs in Fun on Wheels. This means we all treat each other like VIPs, all the time. We do not leave any kid out."

Jed looked over his little pack of bikers. "OK, are we all set? First we will play a game called 'Step by Step.' First step: We will ride two blocks to the left. Then we will stop. Then I will say the next step. You all need to be close when I stop, or you will not know the next step. OK! On your bikes! Get set! Go!"

Block by block, step by step, Jed had the kids ride all about the city, this way and that. Two times they went by places to jump the bikes.

Then, when Jed could see that the kids were doing OK at keeping in a pack, he made up a new game. He called this one "Keep Up with Me." He sped up the pace with that game. They still had to keep close by so they would know where to go.

They ended up at the lake. It was time to go fishing. Next to the lake was an open space with some bike paths. One path led to some cliffs, way up over the lake. Jimmy got on that path with his bike. "I know some great jumps in that open place," he said. "They are way up at the top of the cliffs! Can we go over there? Can we go now?"

The kids all wanted to go up on the cliffs to the big jumps. Jed did not think this was a good plan. Riding on the cliffs was not a good thing for the first day.

"Look, I cannot see the top from here. But over there, I see some jumps. I think those are just fine for us. Do you see them? We can go over there for a while before we go fishing."

"But we want to go up to the top, to the big jumps," said Jimmy. "That will be a lot more fun."

"I know you want to go up there," said Jed, "but it may not be safe, so we will not bike there. The new rule for today is, do not go up on the cliffs. Now, I will race you to those little jumps over there!"

Jed jumped on his bike and raced off, with all the kids right after him. They had a lot of fun jumping and riding in the dust. Then it was time for lunch. Each kid ate a lot! Jimmy had a kick ball in his pack, and they kicked it about on the grass. At last they rented poles and went fishing in the lake.

They were all having fun, and Jed just about lost track of time. It was past two when he remembered to check the time. He yelled out and got the kids to clean up and get set to go. "OK," said Jed. "We are going to have to stick real close to do this. We have to get back fast. Ride close, VIPs! Keep up with me! I know some back ways. We can do it!"

Jed led the way. They snaked in and out of back lots. They went fast on some streets. With a last push, they just made it back to the shop on time. The first mom was just getting there when they rode up. Jed slapped hands with each kid.

After all the kids were picked up, Jed plopped down by Bill. "I am dogged," he said. "That was one long day, but it was fun! I think the kids had fun." Bill smiled and nodded.

It was the end of the camp day, but Jed still had work to do. He had to get set for the next day. Plus he had to keep working at the shop until closing time. All he felt like doing was taking a nap! He made it till closing time. He shut up the shop, rode home, and ate some ham and beans. He fell into bed by 9:00!

5. Jumps and Games

The Fun on Wheels Biking Day Camp was growing. The next week Jed had one more kid. After three weeks the camp was full, with six kids. Each Monday Jed ended the day with a "Be Safe on Your Bike" class. When one of the VIPs had a flat, Jed got out his bike kit and led the kids through the steps of fixing a flat. He was teaching them how to look after their bikes. Jed had fun, and the kids liked the camp.

They looked for all the great places to ride. Some days they rode on city streets. Other times they rode on bike paths that went out of the city. On these trips they rode under big green trees. One bike path led to a creek. Jed and the kids stopped and looked for frogs and little fish. Some days, if there was a breeze, they stopped to fly kites.

Other days they made a game of getting to know the city map. They went up and down each block. They got to know the name of each place in the city and how to get there. Then Jed would make them into two teams. They would play a game called "Get There." Jed named a place, and the team had to tell how to get there. They had to tell which way to go, block by block.

The Fun on Wheels VIPs got to know the city more each day. They looked for places with bumps, dips, little hills, and ramps. They had fun making jumps! Each day, the kids begged Jed to go back by those places. They liked jumping their bikes. Jed planned a little time each day just for bike jumping. He would bring them to a new jump spot each day.

One day Jed had the kids bring their in-line skates. He was going to take them to some places that were great for skating. Just before they got going, Jed remembered one thing. If they went skating, they would need to lock up the bikes. Some of the kids did not have locks. Jed used some of his pocket cash. He got a lock for each kid who did not have one.

This was not the only cash that Jed spent on the kids. He was finding that he needed to keep some things on hand for fixing bikes. It seemed like each day one thing or other needed fixing. And he wanted to have other things on hand. When the kids wanted to fly kites, he spent what he needed to. He got kites for all the kids.

Jed did not know how much cash he was spending this way. He would be taking away some from his car savings. Yet it was not a big deal to him. Doing things for the kids gave him a good feeling. It felt great.

The only part that got him down was that he needed more rest. Being out with the kids all day was a big job. He was wiped out at the end of each camp day. But he still had to work his shift at the shop.

One day, he nodded off to sleep. The shop was still open. No one was there but him. Jed just went to sleep, resting on a bike rack. Just then Bill came in.

"Say, Jed! Wake up, Jed!" said Bill, giving Jed's back a little push.

Jed woke up all of a sudden. He did not know where he was. Then he saw Bill.

"Gosh . . . what? Did I go to sleep?" Jed felt bad.

Bill said, "Jed, I think it is a lot for you to run the day camp and work at the shop. I do not want you to take on more than you can do safely."

"Thanks, Bill," said Jed. "I know it. While I am out with the kids, things are great. But late in the day, I just feel like taking a nap. If no one is here, then I just feel like sleeping!"

"Yes, but that is not a safe thing for the shop, or for you," said Bill. "We may need to cut back on your shop days."

Jed was thinking, I need to work each day. If I do not work, it will cut into my car savings. . . . But he did not say this.

Bill said, "Jed, I will take over this shift for you. Go on home and get some rest. I need you to be well rested for working with the kids. You do not know when you will have to think fast with them."

Jed grinned. "I have to think fast all the time with those kids!"

Bill said, "Go on now. I will close up the shop."

The next day, Jed and the kids were just getting back to the shop. In the bike rack, Jed saw the bike that Amanda rode. Amanda! What was she doing at the bike shop?

Jed dropped his bike. He got the kids off their bikes fast. He ran them into the shop. Amanda was speaking with Bill.

"Amanda! You are not at camp! What . . . ?"

Amanda looked up at Jed. "I have some news, Jed. The camp where I work is going to be closed in two weeks. It has been sold off as a golf place. I will be out of a job! Plus, now a lot of kids will not have a place to go for camp!"

Jed felt bad for Amanda. He remembered the fact that he was working her old days at the bike shop. Bill said, "Thanks for coming in, Amanda. I will let you know if I have an opening."

Then Amanda was out of there. Jed went after her. "Amanda, do you have to go now? Can you hang out for a bit? Did Bill tell you about the biking day camp?"

While the kids were being picked up, Jed and Amanda sat down. Jed wanted to tell her all about Fun on Wheels. He went on and on about the kids and the places they rode. "I am glad things have worked out so well for you here," Amanda said.

Jed could not help thinking about one thing. He had the job Amanda used to have. Now she was out of work. He felt like he should help Amanda. But how?

Jed could not hold back. "Amanda, I feel bad that your job at the camp is ending. I have been working your days at the shop. If you want them back, I will speak to Bill about it."

Amanda could not help smiling. It was so great to see Amanda smile. "That would be great, Jed," she said.

The next day, Jed spoke to Bill.

6. Smash!

The day camp was going great. Amanda was back at the shop. Things were fine for Jed. Then it seemed as if all his luck ran out. He and the kids were stopped next to a car lot. Cars were going in and out. Jimmy had a flat, so Jed dropped his bike to help him fix it. He had all the kids push their bikes over to the side. Just then a big SUV came fast out of the lot. The man driving did not see Jed's bike. Smash! He ran right over the bike with his SUV. The crunching sound made Jed feel sick. Jed jumped to his feet, but the man just kept going. "Stop!" Jed yelled. "You ran over a bike!" The man in the SUV drove off fast.

Jed and the kids looked at the bike. It was a mess. The frame was twisted. The wheels were bent. No way could he ride it. Jed was thinking, Now what? This is bad, real bad. I need a bike to run the camp. If I do not have a bike, what will happen?

He picked up the smashed bike. He would have to drag it back to the shop. The kids felt bad about Jed's bike. "Bum deal," Kenny said. The others nodded. Jed had the kids push their bikes back with him. They were late getting back. Moms and dads were there, not knowing what made their kids late. They looked mad till they saw Jed's bike.

Jed said, "We had some bad luck on the way back to the shop. All the kids are OK. It is just my bike that got mashed."

Amanda came out of the shop. She helped Jed get the kids checked in. After a bit, they all went off with their moms and dads. When the last kid left, Jed slumped down by his crushed bike.

"I do not know what I am going to do now," said Jed. "I will need to get a new bike right now, if the camp is to keep going. We cannot have a biking day camp if the lead VIP does not have a bike!"

"You are in the right place to get a new bike, you know," said Amanda. "We must have 50 or 60 bikes here right now."

"Yes, but I am saving my cash for a car," said Jed. "I did not plan on spending it on a new bike! These bikes cost a lot—one for me would be, what, $300.00—or more!"

Amanda said, "Jed, save your $300.00. I have a bike. I will let you ride it for now. Here it is. See, it is not so bad a bike. I can drive my car to work for a time."

Jed did not know what to say. Amanda had just saved him! He said, "Thanks, Amanda—you do not know what that means to me."

"It will cost you big time!" teased Amanda. "Now I have one on you. And you had best not get my bike smashed, or it will be all over for you!"

Jed looked back at Amanda. "No way!" he said.

Amanda and Jed kept chatting. She was over being sad about her camp. Now she was thinking about a day camp for next year—Fun on Wheels day camp. She had all kinds of plans for how to make Fun on Wheels more fun. Jed gulped. He had not been thinking at all about next year!

Then Amanda said, "I bet the kids would like to go camping. They could sleep out under the open sky. It would be big fun for them. You know, one or two times each week."

"Yes, but where?" asked Jed. He could not think of a place to take the kids camping.

"There must be a place. We . . . I mean you . . . could find one. I just think it would be fun, is all!" said Amanda. "Could be there is a ranch or some open place like that. I think there must be a place where camping out would be OK."

On the way home, Jed kept thinking about the things Amanda had said. On one hand, she had some great plans. On the other hand, he was thinking, why is Amanda telling me these things? She is going on and on like she is part of the biking day camp. What does she want from it? Does she want my job?

All the next week, Jed wanted to speak to Bill about the bike camp for next year. But he held back. He did not say a thing. Part of him was thinking that Bill liked Amanda more than him. Would Bill like to have Amanda run the Fun on Wheels camp, not him? Jed kept still. He liked this job. He wanted to keep it.

7. A Bad Call

"I said NO!" snapped Jed. "No way are we going up to those cliffs."

The kids whined, "Why not?" Jimmy stomped and tossed a rock. They kept begging to go up to the top of the cliffs. They wanted to ride on the big jumps up there. Jed liked to ride on big jumps. He liked that a lot. But he had six kids with him. He did not want them to ride up by the cliffs. It did not feel safe.

"We have a lot of places to jump down at the flat part," said Jed. "We can ride those jumps and the little hills all we want."

Jimmy said, "Those are no good! Little kids can do those. We have wanted to go up to the real jumps for weeks. We are good with our bikes. Now it is time for us to jump the big jumps."

It was the same thing each time they rode to the lake. Each time, the kids wanted to go up by the cliffs. Each time, Jed said no. To Jed, this game was no fun. More than that, some days he was not that into riding with the kids at all! He wished he had a day in the week just to hang out with other dudes.

It was close to the end of Fun on Wheels Biking Day Camp. The days were long and hot. Jed still had eight more days left with the kids. He could not help thinking about the fun he was missing with his pals.

Then Jed saw Jimmy take off up the path to the cliffs. "Back up, Jimmy Jump!" yelled Jed. "No riding on the cliffs! Come on, we can lock up the bikes over there. We are going fishing!" Jed had the kids lock up their bikes. They went to rent poles. The heat was very bad on this day. Jed spotted some shade under a tree by the water. In a bit, Jed and the kids were fishing at the little beach.

Just then, some of Jed's pals came driving up in a car. They were all set to go swimming. They waved to Jed and yelled, "Come on, Jed! You work too hard! Swim with us, dude!"

Man, did Jed want to go with them!

It was about time to eat. Jed got all the kids in one place. He looked out at the rocks where his pals were leaping and diving and having fun.

He was thinking, "What could happen if I just went over there to swim for a little bit? These kids have been safe all these weeks. They are good kids. I can leave them for a while. Why not?"

Jed could not stand it any more. He told the kids, "You all keep right here. You can eat and then rest for a little bit. The bikes are OK—they are all locked up. I will be right back. And keep out of the water! Can you do that?"

The kids were eating. They nodded yes.

Jed ran as fast as he could over to the rocks. Just before he jumped in, he looked back over at the beach at the VIPs. They were still sitting there, eating. Jed leaped right off one of the rocks. He splashed into the cold water. Yes! That felt good! How long had it been? He could not remember when he last went diving with his pals. Not this year at all.

Jed made six more quick leaps and dives. Then he ran back to the place where he left the kids. When he got there, he said, "OK, we can take these fishing poles back to the pole shack."

Then he stopped. What—or who—was missing? There were only four kids.

"Where are Kenny and Jimmy?" he asked. They must be right here, he was thinking. I was only diving for a little while.

"Did you see where they went?" he asked. The other kids grunted "No" and did not look at Jed.

Now Jed did not feel happy. In fact, he felt sick. He felt bad that he had left the kids. What if

Kenny and Jimmy went in the water? What if they needed help? How well could they swim? Some very bad things were running through his thinking now: "What could have happened? No, no, no. This is like a bad dream, and I made it bad. What now?"

Jed looked out on the lake. He and the kids ran up and down the beach. They went over to the fishing pole shack. Jimmy and Kenny were not there. They scanned the water one more time. They yelled out, "Kenny! Jimmy!" No one yelled back. Jed was thinking that some very bad thing could have happened to them. What if they went down in the water and did not come back up?

Then Jed remembered the bikes. Could those two be over there? He and the other kids ran over to the bikes. Kenny and Jimmy were not there. But what was this? Two bikes were missing. Jimmy and Kenny must be on their bikes!

"Where did those two ride off to?" Now Jed was mad. He yanked his bike out of the rack. He remembered the cliffs. He was thinking, The place with the big jumps! I bet that is where they are!

Jed and the VIPs raced on their bikes over to the open space. That did no good. They could not see the top of the cliffs.

Now what could he do? He needed to ride up there to look for them. But he could not just leave the other kids. Leaving the kids was what got him in this bad spot! Still, he had to go up to the top of those cliffs.

Jed felt stuck. What a mess he had made of things! He could not go looking for Jimmy and Kenny. But he could not just sit still. Jed was thinking, "What if a bad thing happens to those two kids? If it does, I will not get over it. How could I have done this?"

8. On the Cliffs

"Jed! Jed!" Jed looked up. He saw . . . Amanda! It was like she had come out of the sky to help him. And man, did he need help! "I am so glad to see you," Jed said. "But what are you doing here?"

"Bill said you would be here with the kids," she said. "So I came looking for you. I wanted to see what you do all day with these kids."

"You have been looking for us?" yelled Jed. "We have been looking for two lost VIPs! Kenny and Jimmy went off on their bikes when I was not there. Now we cannot find them."

He got off to one side with Amanda. "I feel so bad, Amanda," said Jed. "This is my doing. I left the kids for just a bit. I went to dive off the rocks, just for a while! I know it was not right. And now this has happened!"

"How can I help?" asked Amanda.

"I need to go up to the cliffs right now," Jed said. "I think those two are up there. Will you look after the other kids while I go?"

"Do not say one thing more," said Amanda. "Just go. I will be here with the kids."

Jed jumped on his bike and pushed up the steep hill. He made it to the top of the open place. He zipped right over to the cliffs. It was very steep there. The path was right next to the lip of a cliff. He looked over the side. He did not see the kids down there. This time he was glad not to see them! He kept going up to the very top. He pushed his legs as fast as they could go.

At the very top, he stopped. There they were! Kenny and Jimmy were jumping their bikes on the big jumps. Jed felt very happy, and then very mad!

"Kenny! Jimmy! You two! What are you doing up here!"

Jimmy and Kenny saw Jed. They stopped riding. They looked down at their feet.

"You know the rules!" Jed said. "I said stay with all the kids. I said this is not a place to go! I said no jumping on the cliffs! So what are you doing up here jumping on the cliffs? Tell me that."

Kenny and Jimmy kept looking down. "We just wanted to try it," Jimmy said.

"Well, you did," Jed said. "And now you are going back to the shop."

Jed did not know what he felt most—mad or glad. He got Jimmy and Kenny down the path and back to the flats as fast as he could. They were OK. He was glad about that. He was mad at them as well. But mostly he was mad at what he did.

At the base of the hill, the other VIPs were riding their bikes on the little jumps. Amanda was standing to the side. When she saw Kenny and Jimmy with Jed, she looked happy. Things could have been very, very bad, but all was OK.

Amanda helped Jed get the VIPs on their way back to the shop. Then Jed and the kids rode next to her as she went over to her car. Jed said, "Amanda, you saved the day just now. I did not know what I was going to do. . . ."

"OK, OK, we can just add this to what I have over you!" teased Amanda. "I have saved you more than one time this year!"

On the ride back to the shop, Jed kept thinking about how Amanda kept helping him. He remembered what she had said about the day camp next year. Those were neat plans. Going camping with the kids under the trees or by a creek—that could be great! And what about just now, at the lake? If Amanda had not been there, who knows what would have happened?

Jed could see that he had not been right at all about Amanda. Why did he think she wanted to take over his job? She wanted to help! She was just that way.

Jed made a new plan right then: I will speak to Bill about Amanda. I will tell him she is great with this day camp thing. I will see if Bill would like two people to run the camp next year.

9. Feeling Rich

Jed sat on his bed. He added up the cash that he had saved over the past 16 weeks.

The bike he needed was going to cost him. Still, Bill would give him a good rate on a trade-in. It would be a bit less than a new bike. Running the camp had cost quite a bit. But Jed had saved a lot of what he made. He added things up. Jed had $2,300.00. He was thinking, Take away the $100.00 the bike will cost . . .

Jed could see that he was close to having what he needed. At least he could go and look for a car now. He had to have more cash to keep it running. But that would come. He had the part-time job at the bike shop for the school year.

Jed smiled. He felt rich. But it was not the cash. It was not the car he would get. The car was a big deal, that was so. But Jed felt rich about other things. He felt good about his job at the bike shop. It was a neat place to work. He felt rich about the weeks and weeks of day camp. And the kids? His little pack of bike riding pals? They were all VIPs to him. And he felt so fine about what he had worked out with Amanda. What a blast camp was going to be next year!